by Richard C. Lawrence
illustrated by Remy Simard

Scott Foresman

Editorial Offices: Glenview, Illinois • New York, New York
Sales Offices: Reading, Massachusetts • Duluth, Georgia
Glenview, Illinois • Carrollton, Texas • Menlo Park, California

So you are going into space! We did it. Now we live on a new planet and we like it a lot! That's why they call us Kids in Space!

Starring...
Kids in Space!

We want you to be happy on your new planet too. Let Kids in Space show you how!

First of all, don't be late for your spaceship! The next one might not come for a long, long time.

Next, don't take too many things
with you. Spaceships don't have
much room. But you can take as
many books as you want. They can
all fit in one of your hands!

When you get on board the
spaceship, try to get a window seat.
That way, you will be able to see all
the great things in the sky—moons,
stars, and planets!

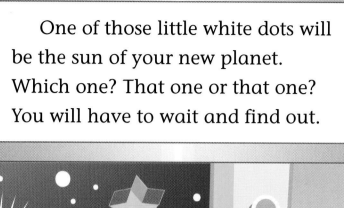

One of those little white dots will be the sun of your new planet. Which one? That one or that one? You will have to wait and find out.

When you land on your new planet, act cool. Say something like, "Nice planet" or "This looks just like the last planet we landed on."

Keep your space suit and helmet on
when you go outside! They will help
you breathe. It's a good idea to put your
name on your space suit. That way,
people can tell who you are!

Bring things to do in case your space cart breaks down. Someone will come to fix it.

Max's Space Fix-It

Playing ball is very different on some planets. You might be lighter than on Earth. You might be able to throw a ball, and jump, and kick . . . farther than ever before!

On a big planet, everything weighs more than it does on Earth. It's hard to run fast on a big planet. It's hard to jump far on a big planet.

But don't worry. On a heavy
planet, you will have fun getting
stronger.

Which kind of planet would you
like to live on?

Everyone likes to talk about the planets they have visited. That's a good way to make friends in space. But there is one planet everyone likes to talk about best. Earth!

There are many things to do in space. But when you're there, don't forget about Earth!

We talk about Earth all the time. We even dream about it.

That's how you can tell we are Kids in Space!